George and Flora's Secret Garden

M&S

Jam

GEORGE AND
FLORA'S SECRET
GARDEN

To Kate, who helped inspire this book
and our young (and not so young) gardening research team:
Jake, Charlie, Jack, Meg, Hugh, Martha, Daisy and Ruby.
JE and LHR

Marks and Spencer plc
PO Box 3339
Chester CH99 9QS

shop online
www.marksandspencer.com

First published in the UK by Eden Project Books, 2010
This edition published exclusively for Marks and Spencer plc, 2012

ISBN 978-1-9058-1197-7
Printed in China

George and Flora's Secret Garden

Jo Elworthy
Illustrated by Ley Honor Roberts

M&S

It was a chilly day in January and George and Flora
had just come in from Grandpa's garden.
"We've got some important news for you," said
Mum and Dad. "We're going to have a baby!"

"Whoopee!" said Flora.

"When?" asked George.

"In about six months," said Mum.

"That means Baby will arrive in July."

"But that's **AGES!**" cried George
and Flora together.

"It's only February. Baby won't be here for five more months!" sighed Flora.
"Waiting is so boring!" said George.

"Why don't we keep busy by planning something nice
for when Baby comes?" suggested Grandpa.
"A party!" cried Flora.
"A den!" shouted George.
Grandpa laughed. "How about both? We can grow the
food for the party and build a den right here in my garden."
"And keep it all a big secret!" giggled Flora, who loved secrets.

FEBRUARY

Dig compost into the soil. This makes it crumbly and adds food for the plants.

Getting Ready

Making Compost

Turn plant waste into plant food!

Dead stems
Weeds
Shredded newspaper
Grass cuttings
Vegetable peelings

1. Chop up your waste.
2. Mix it up.
3. Put in compost bin.
4. Cover with lid.
5. Red stripy worms and bugs turn mixture into compost.

Your compost will be ready in about six months!

BABY NEWS

Mum is 20 weeks pregnant.

She is eating well to feed Baby, who is growing inside her. She sometimes feels a bit tired and sick.

SEEDS

Strawberries
Seed Potatoes
Tomatoes
Sunflowers
Pumpkins
Sweetcorn
Leafy Salad

Willow

SEED & POTTING COMPOST

Grandpa took George and Flora to buy seeds for their secret garden.
Flora had a list. "Strawberries, potatoes, tomatoes and sunflowers,
a pumpkin for Halloween, sweetcorn for corn on the cob and
leafy salad, because grown-ups are always telling us how
yummy it is."
"Grandpa," sighed George, "what about our den?"

"No problem," said Grandpa. "We'll buy some willow, a hammer and these nails." George decided that garden centres were OK after all!

OUR DEN

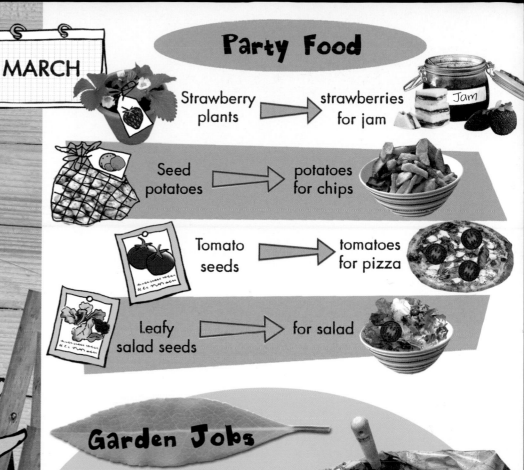

Party Food

Strawberry plants → strawberries for jam

Seed potatoes → potatoes for chips

Tomato seeds → tomatoes for pizza

Leafy salad seeds → for salad

MARCH

Garden Jobs

- Seed **potatoes** are special potatoes for planting.

- Put them in a box or tray.

- After a month they'll grow little shoots. Then they can be planted outside.

- Fill pot with seed compost.
- Add a **tomato** seed.
- Cover it up with compost.

Now put your box and your pots on a sunny window sill.

BABY NEWS

Mum is 24 weeks pregnant.

Her tummy is getting big so she needs to buy larger clothes!

April arrived, and George and Flora started to plan their garden.
"We'll need lots of strawberries," said Flora, "in case the birds eat some."
"My potatoes will be OK," said George. "They grow underground and I'll keep a lookout from the den."
"Let's have a competition to grow the tallest sunflower," said Flora.
"Don't forget to plant one for Baby," said Grandpa.

Garden Jobs

Outside:

RAKE
Dig, then rake soil until crumbly. Dig a row of holes.

PLANT

Turn each strawberry plant upside down and remove pot. Place plant, roots-down, into hole. Pat down earth gently around plants.

Put each potato in a hole and cover completely with soil.

SOW

Sow leafy salad seeds thinly in rows in the soil outside. Follow the instructions on the packet.

Inside:

Sow sunflowers, pumpkins and sweetcorn in pots, just like you did with your tomato seeds. Put them in a warm, sunny place.

BABY NEWS
Mum is 28 weeks pregnant. Baby inside her is growing fast and is now about the size of a bag of flour.

Each day, as it started to get warmer, George and Flora raced over to Grandpa's house.

"I'm on watering duty," cried Flora.

"Look – the sunflower shoots are coming up!"

"We'll be able to plant them soon," said Grandpa.

GEORGE AND FLORA'S SECRET GARDEN

"And start on our den!"
said George.

Garden News

Inside and outside, all the seeds are growing into seedlings!

Bad Guys

Good Guys

SLUGS chomp leaves.

TOADS scoff slugs.

APHIDS suck juice from stems.

Keep a look out for garden creatures. Some may be after your plants!

LADYBIRDS munch aphids.

Den Building

1. Make poles into tripods and tie with string.

2. Place tripods where you want your den.

3. Tie a pole across the top.

4. Tie or nail slats to your tripod to make it stronger.

5. Plant willow stems. These will grow roots and make a living, growing wall!

BABY NEWS

Mum is 30 weeks pregnant.

George and Flora can feel Baby moving!

Two weeks later, Flora planted their sunflowers out.
"Mine's the tallest," she said.
Typical, thought George. "Grandpa, my pumpkins
are growing so slowly," he sighed.

"Be patient," replied Grandpa. "Growing things takes time. They'll be a few months yet, just like Baby."

GEORGE AND FLORA'S SECRET GARDEN

Garden Jobs

Gather leafy salad to eat!

Water . . . weed . . . feed . . . and measure . . . . . . your plants!

1. Plant out tomato, sunflower, pumpkin and sweetcorn plants – like you did with your strawberries.

2. Tie your tomato and sunflower plants to canes to support them as they grow.

3. Pile earth around your potato shoots to help them grow new little potatoes underground.

BABY NEWS

Mum is now 32 weeks pregnant. Mum's tummy moves as Baby wriggles about.

All summer, George and Flora helped Grandpa in the garden.

"Baby will be born in a few weeks," said Flora.

"I know!" said George, excitedly. "Keep weeding!"

Just then, Mum arrived to pick them up . . . and she was early!

"Quick!" gasped George. "Hide the spade, hide the den,
hide the pumpkin, hide the garden!"

JUNE

Summer

Tie to canes
as they grow taller.

Pick, eat and sow
some more.

Weed and feed with
garden compost.

Pick and eat some.
Make jam too!

Water, weed, feed and
keep an eye out for pests
eating your plants!

Water
them if the
soil gets
too dry.

Den Building

Add the
finishing
touches to
your den.

Welcome

OUR DEN

Luckily Flora had a plan.
"Hello, Mum, you
look tired. Let's
go inside and
get a drink."
"Phew," said George.
"That was close."

BABY NEWS

Mum is 36 weeks
pregnant. She is
getting everything
clean, tidy and
ready for Baby.

At last it was July and Baby arrived!
George and Flora brought some daisies from the secret garden.
"Hello, Baby," they said. "We've got lots to show you!"

"Dad and I were thinking of calling your baby sister Daisy," said Mum. "What do you think?"
"Perfect!" said Grandpa.
"Hello, Daisy," laughed George and Flora.

When Daisy was one month old, Mum and Dad brought her to Grandpa's for lunch. "Surprise!" shouted George and Flora.

Welcome

OUR DEN

Sweetcorn

Salad

Sweetcorn

Chips

Pizza

Jam sandwiches

"Welcome to our secret garden!"

"Oh, this is lovely," said Mum.

"When can Daisy have her own plate of food?" asked George.

"Soon," replied Mum.

"That means ages," George whispered to Flora.

GEORGE AND FLORA'S SECRET GARDEN

Party Time!

Time to make yummy picnic treats from the food you've grown!

Perfect Picnic Pizza!

You will need:

Pizza base
1 tablespoon of olive oil
1 clove of garlic
6 large tomatoes
Teaspoon of mixed herbs
Pinch of pepper
100g grated cheese
Oven – heated to 190°C / 375°F / gas mark 5

Ask a grown-up to help you with the chopping and cooking parts!

1. Chop the garlic and tomatoes into tiny pieces.

2. Heat the olive oil in a saucepan and fry the garlic for two minutes.

3. Add the chopped tomatoes, herbs and pepper. Mix well and cook for another three minutes.

4. Spread some tomato mixture onto your pizza base.

5. Sprinkle cheese on top.

6. Add your favourite topping.

7. Cook in the oven for 15 minutes.

BABY NEWS

Daisy is a month old. She sleeps lots and only drinks Mum's milk.

In the autumn, Mum came to Grandpa's to help harvest
the vegetables and to judge the sunflower competition.
"Daisy is the winner!" she said.
"First prize is this HUMUNGOUS pumpkin!" cried George.

"When can Daisy eat it?" asked Flora.
"Soon," replied Mum.
Daisy looked at George and Flora and smiled.

TOP SECRET

GEORGE AND FLORA'S SECRET GARDEN

SEPTEMBER and OCTOBER

Harvest

POTATOES
Bake them or make into chips!

TOMATOES
Eat them fresh or in a pasta sauce!

LEAFY SALAD
Fresh and healthy.

SWEETCORN
Tasty with butter and pepper!

SUNFLOWERS
Eat some seeds and save some to sow next year!

PUMPKINS
Great in pies or soups!

Carve a pumpkin.

Why not give It a scary face!

BABY NEWS

In October Daisy is three months old. She smiles, gurgles and recognizes people.

Winter arrived.

"Our garden hasn't got much in it," said Flora.

"Don't worry," said Grandpa.

"The plants will grow again in the spring."

"Daisy is still growing," said Flora.

"She's got teeth now."

"She'll be able to eat something – soon," added George cheekily.

Garden Jobs

Time to tidy your garden. If you have bushes and trees, help a grown-up cut off any dead branches.

Hang up left-over sunflower heads. Hungry birds will eat the seeds.

Gather branches and twigs for a bonfire. Sweep up leaves.

In December Daisy is five months old. She can roll over and has grown her first tooth.

BABY NEWS

Daisy sleeps through the night . . . sometimes!

GEORGE AND FLORA'S SECRET GARDEN

Then it was January again. Dad was dishing out pumpkin soup for lunch.
"Is that Daisy's pumpkin?" asked George.
"Can Daisy have some too?" asked Flora.

Flora's garden

"Yes, it is, and yes, she can," said Mum.
They all waited while Daisy had
her first taste of the secret garden.
"Whoopee!" shouted George and Flora.
Yum, thought Daisy.

corn

tree
house

George

slide

tomato sauce

ice cream

money tree

chips

PLANT
(outside in garden)
APRIL

EAT
JUNE and JULY

Strawberries

PLANT
(outside in garden)
APRIL

EAT
JUNE to
OCTOBER

Potatoes

SOW
(outside in garden)
APRIL to
SEPTEMBER

EAT
6 weeks later from
MAY to
OCTOBER

Leafy salad

SOW
(outside in garden)
APRIL - JULY

EAT
JULY - NOVEMBER

Spinach beet

SOW
(inside in pots)
APRIL

PLANT
(outside in garden)
MAY

EAT
AUGUST to
SEPTEMBER

Sweetcorn

SOW
(outside in garden)
MARCH to JUNE

EAT
3 months later from
JUNE to
SEPTEMBER

Peas

Jam

SOW
(outside in garden)
APRIL

EAT
SEPTEMBER to
FEBRUARY

Leeks

SOW
(inside in pots)
MARCH

PLANT
(inside in bigger pots
or outside in garden)
MAY

EAT
JULY to SEPTEMBER

Tomatoes

SOW
(outside in garden)
APRIL

EAT
JUNE to
OCTOBER

Carrots

SOW
(inside in pots)
APRIL

PLANT
(outside in garden)
MAY

EAT
SEPTEMBER to
JANUARY

Pumpkins

SOW
(outside in garden)
APRIL

EAT
NOVEMBER to
MARCH

Winter Cabbages

SOW
(inside in pots)
APRIL

PLANT
(outside in garden)
MAY

ENJOY
AUGUST and
SEPTEMBER

Sunflowers